writing guides

ACTIVITIES FOR WRITING

Adventure STORIES

GUY MERCHANT

PHOTOCOPIABLE PHOTOCOPIABLE PHOTOCOPIABLE PHOTOCOPIABLE

FICTION
FOR AGES
7-9

CONTENTS

INTRODUCTION

The Scholastic *Writing Guides* series provides teachers with ideas and projects that promote a range of writing, bringing insights from educational research into the classroom. Each guide explores a different type of writing and provides example material, background information, photocopiable activities and teaching suggestions. Their aim is to enable teachers to guide the writing process, share planning ideas and develop themes as a context for writing activities.

The materials:
- motivate children with interesting activities
- break complex types of writing into manageable teaching units
- focus on and develop the typical features of particular types of writing
- provide original approaches to teaching.

Each book is divided into sections, beginning with examples of the type of writing being taught. These are followed by ideas for developing writing and projects that will extend over a series of sessions.

SECTION ONE: USING GOOD EXAMPLES

Section One looks at good examples of the genre, with the emphasis on using texts to stimulate and develop writing. Two example texts are shared, and questions that focus the discussion on their significant features are suggested. This is followed by activities that explore what the texts can teach us about writing, enabling teachers to compare the two texts and to go on to model the type of writing presented in the guide.

SECTION TWO: DEVELOPING WRITING

Section Two moves from reading to writing. This section provides activities that prompt and support children in planning and writing. A range of approaches includes planning templates and strategies to stimulate ideas. The activities refine children's ideas about the type of writing being developed and give them focused writing practice in the context of scaffolded tasks. Teacher's notes support each activity by explaining the objective and giving guidance on delivery.

SECTION THREE: WRITING

Section Three moves on to writing projects. Building upon the earlier work in Section Two, these projects aim to develop the quality of writing and provide a selection of ideas for class or group work on a particular theme or idea. The teacher may choose to use some or all of the ideas presented in each project as a way of weaving the strategies developed in Section Two into a more complex and extended writing task.

SECTION FOUR: REVIEW

Section Four supports the assessment process. Children are encouraged to reflect on the type of writing they are tackling and to evaluate how effectively their work has met the criteria for the genre identified in Section One.

The Catcher

Breathless she came to a halt, and bowed to her invisible partner. Then, above the sound of her own breathing she heard a rustling and snapping of twigs, and looked into the copse beyond and saw a figure go striding by. It was there and gone in a trice, hidden by the trees, but Polly saw it for long enough to know that this was no ordinary visitor, come to feed the birds or walk the dog.

The man (for she saw that it was a man) went with long bounding strides – scissoring through the bracken – and yet there was a curious dreamlike slowness to his movements, as in a film show in slow motion. He might have been treading on air. And raised in his right arm was a long rod and a – "*Net*?" Polly shook her head to settle it. Who would go striding through the woods at evening with a huge net, as if to catch some mysterious quarry?

"Not for butterflies," she thought, "nor even birds. Much too big."

Again she shook her head.

"Must've dreamed it," she thought. "All that twizzling."

from *The Secret World of Polly Flint* by Helen Cresswell

To be a Firework-Maker

"That's what happens to those who don't come prepared!" said Razvani. "But now you must submit yourself as they did. Walk into my flames, Lila! You have come for the Royal Sulphur – receive it from my hands!"

And he laughed louder, and spun in a rapid dance, stamping his feet in a wide circle and causing a ring of fire to blaze up around him. Through the lashing red and yellow and orange, his face seemed to waver and flicker, but his voice rang out clearly over the roar and crackle:

"You want to be a Firework-Maker? Walk into my flames! Your father did in his time, and so did every artist in fire. This is what you've come for! Why are you waiting?"

She was terribly afraid. But she knew that she must do it; she would rather be a ghost than go back empty-handed and fail at the one thing she had ever wanted.

So she took one step forward, and then another, and her poor feet burned and blistered so that she cried out loud. Then she took another step, and when she knew she could bear it no longer she heard a great sound behind her, like a mighty trumpet. And through the blaze a voice was shouting:

"Lila! The water! Take it, take it!"

from *The Firework-Maker's Daughter* by Philip Pullman

SECTION ONE

USING GOOD EXAMPLES

Adventure stories are written to entertain and excite. Strong and interesting main characters, with whom we can identify, are placed in difficult or dangerous situations and readers 'live dangerously' through them. Physical or psychological challenges are overcome as these characters solve problems or complete quests. Excitement and tension are built up through changes of pace, as main characters are trapped but escape in the nick of time; chase and are chased; hide, jump, climb; and confront their enemies. As readers and writers, children can work imaginatively with adventure stories, drawing on film and television narratives to describe action, tension and excitement.

Shared activities

The Catcher

This story tells of a lonely girl's adventures in a hidden/secret world. This extract describes her first sighting of the much-feared character referred to later as the Catcher. Polly has just been practising some dance steps (this is the *twizzling*) when the Catcher appears. The first paragraph creates intrigue and suspense by focusing on the senses – the sound of Polly's breathing and twigs snapping. Adjectives describing the Catcher add depth – he is *no ordinary visitor* and moves *with a curious dreamlike slowness*. Questions that help us to identify with Polly's feelings add mystery.

Before reading photocopiable page 4, explain how Polly has been dancing – *twizzling* – with an imaginary partner. Read the extract together and talk about the figure Polly has just seen. How did he move? Why might he carry such a large net? Ask the children what adventure this could lead to for Polly. Talk about what sorts of things can happen in an adventure story like this.

To be a Firework-Maker

Lila faces all sorts of dangers in her quest for the secrets of firework-making. In this extract, she has reached the cave of Razvani, the great Fire-Fiend. To become a Firework-Maker, Lila needs Razvani's Royal Sulphur – but he isn't going to make it easy for her. The menacing figure of Razvani taunts Lila with his laughter as he repeatedly challenges her to *'walk into my flames!'* After reading photocopiable page 5, ask the children how they would feel if they were Lila. Draw attention to words and phrases that describe the setting, including the sounds. Encourage the children to read out Razvani's speech, putting expression and menace into his voice. Will Lila succeed? Are adventure heroes and heroines always brave in the face of danger?

Who was that?

Display an enlarged copy of photocopiable page 4. With the children's help, use different colours to underline words and phrases that describe what Polly hears and sees. Record these on a display copy of photocopiable page 8. Ask the children to work in pairs to think of ways to describe how Polly feels, then record the best of these ideas on the bottom part of photocopiable page 8. Now ask the children for suggestions of what might happen after the end of this extract.

Walk into my flames!

Display an enlarged copy of photocopiable page 5 and re-read the extract, asking the children to consider Lila's feelings. Should she turn back or face the danger? Why is she so determined? Use photocopiable page 9 and the prompting phrases around the frame to start the discussion. Record the discussion on the board, for instance *If Lila turns back she would return to safety, but fail in her mission. Walking into the flames is dangerous, but it is a test and she really wants the Royal Sulphur.*

writing guides: ADVENTURE STORIES

Taking ideas further

So far, this section has helped you to introduce some important aspects of adventure story writing. Activities have focused on suspense, danger and mystery, and the effect that these can have on the reader. Many children will have a rich experience of this kind of story from television and film, and it is important to draw on this. You may find it useful to look at a short extract from a film like Atlantis: The Lost Empire *or* Jumanji. *This will give more clues about the characteristics of adventure stories and can be used to develop ideas for settings. After looking at a video extract, you can ask the children to list words and phrases that describe the settings. These can then be used for modelling composition in shared writing.*

How does it feel?

This activity looks at different ways in which adventure stories excite the reader. The first example draws on the Polly Flint extract (photocopiable page 4) in which curiosity and tension accompany the appearance of a mysterious character. The second draws on the passage from *The Firework-Maker's Daughter* (photocopiable page 5) in which the main character is in danger and facing a daunting challenge. Other adventure scenarios are then presented and the children need to consider the effect of these on the reader. Encourage them to think about what they would be trying to achieve if they were including these incidents in their story. After discussion and shared writing, children could work on this activity independently.

Adventure soup

Photocopiable page 11 draws together some of the main features of adventure stories and is a guide that can be displayed throughout these activities. You could enlarge it to make a poster or give children individual copies. It can be used to remind them of what they have learned, as well as to evaluate their own or each other's stories.

Extension ideas

Build up a collection of objects that 'belong' to an adventure character. Use these as clues about who the character is, the quest or journey to be undertaken, and what he or she is like. (For example, there may be a rucksack containing a map of Turkey, an old book, a torch, some binoculars, a torn-up letter and an old photograph.) The children could record their ideas about the character, writing words and sentences on a large outline of the figure.

Three-dimensional modelling is a useful way for children to explore settings and you can do this by creating table-top displays or a 'small world' in a shoebox. Models of people can help to bring these to life. Adventure settings could include mysterious buildings, ruined cities and dramatic natural features like dense forests and steep cliffs.

Children's experience of adventure films is a useful discussion tool. (You could look at video extracts, talk about *Spy Kids* and so on.) Some computer games also draw on the adventure story genre, such as *Tomb Raider*. It is important to encourage the use of strong female role models.

Non-fiction material can be an excellent source for ideas of possible dangers. There is no shortage of books on dangerous animals, dinosaurs, ancient mysteries and rainforests that can provide information and inspiration when thinking about unusual and dramatic settings.

It is worth considering making cross-curricular links with land forms as a geography topic to provide extra detail when describing settings.

Who was that?

Polly Flint has just watched the mysterious Catcher passing by.
How does Helen Cresswell describe this event?

What does
Polly hear?

What does
she see?

What might
happen next?

How do you
think Polly feels?

writing guides: **ADVENTURE STORIES**

Walk into my flames!

Lila has to walk through the flames to get the Royal Sulphur…
or maybe she should just go back home. How would she feel if
she turned back now? What will happen if she goes forward?
How will she feel then?

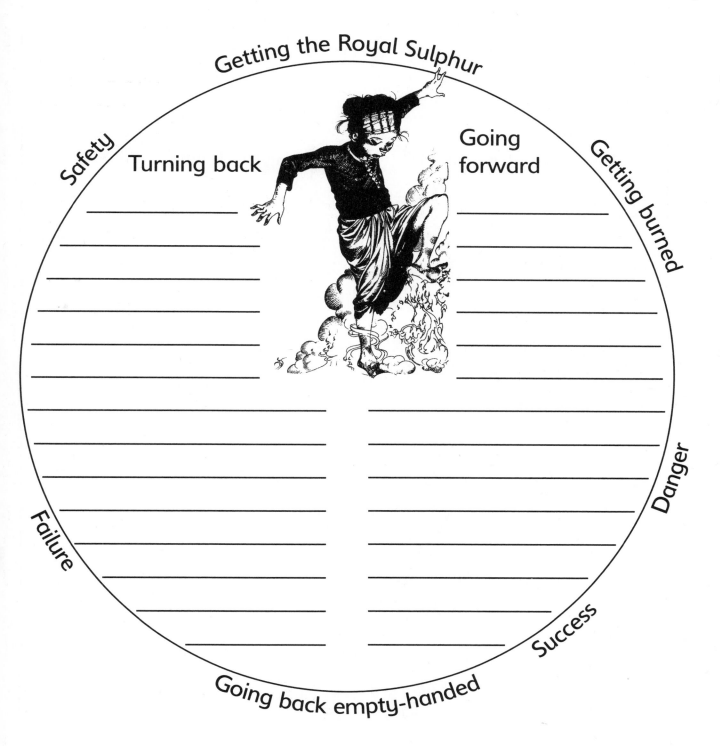

Getting the Royal Sulphur

Safety

Turning back

Going forward

Getting burned

_____

_____

_____

_____

_____

_____

_____

_____

_____

_____

_____

_____

_____

_____

_____

_____

_____

_____

_____

_____

Danger

Failure

Success

Going back empty-handed

How does it feel?

A good adventure story entertains the reader. Think of different ways of doing this to complete the strips on the right. How do you want your reader to feel?

You introduce a mysterious character…	…the reader wants to know who it is.
The main character is in danger…	…the reader is worried.
The setting is dark and cold…	…the reader feels _____ _____ _____
The journey is long and difficult…	…the reader _____ _____ _____
Your main character is being chased…	…the reader _____ _____ _____
Your main character returns home….	…the reader _____ _____ _____

Adventure soup

serves many readers – ideal for entertaining

Ingredients

Characters:	Nice ones and thoroughly nasty ones!
A task or two:	Somewhere to go, something to do.
A trigger:	Something to get your story going.
Danger:	Lots of tricky situations.
Suspense:	What will happen next? Keep them guessing!

And lots of… **ACTION**

Method

1. First prepare your main characters. Make sure they are sweet and strong – just like you! Then add a tasty task or two – perhaps a journey, someone to save, treasure to find, evil to destroy – but don't give too much away.
2. Now think of a trigger. This could be an event, a message, an object or a visitor that gets the story started.
3. Next you need plenty of action. Thicken the plot with heaps of danger. Sprinkle with suspense. Turn up the heat and then dish out your adventure!

SECTION TWO
DEVELOPING WRITING

This section provides guidance on the first stages of creating an adventure story. This work can be an individual or a group project. Whichever you choose, the children will need to pay close attention to planning and organisation. Successful adventure stories need a good plot structure with scope for action and excitement. The children will need to practise specific techniques without losing sight of the overall shape of the story, and the activities in this section are designed to support this process. The first five help children to make decisions about the story as a whole; the others provide opportunities for experimenting with adventure story writing techniques.

OBJECTIVES
■ To understand the key features of an adventure story.
■ To explore how adventure stories entertain the reader.

INTRODUCING ADVENTURE STORY WRITING
WHAT YOU NEED
Strips of paper, writing materials, Blu-Tack, board or flip chart.

WHAT TO DO
Before you start this session, write the aim of the project on the board: 'To write an exciting adventure story'. Decide which aspects of the project will require children to collaborate and which will be individually completed. Also consider the audience for the children's writing. You may have already decided on this (for example, children in another school or a similar age range in your own school) or you might want this to be part of your discussion.

Begin by explaining the purpose of the writing project, reminding the children how they will be drawing on what they have learned from the activities in Section One, as well as developing new writing techniques. Organise the children to work in pairs. Give each pair five or six strips of paper and tell them to jot down things that their audience would like to read about in an adventure story. Provide a few examples, such as a motorbike chase on an icy road; being captured by bandits; escaping from a pit of snakes. After a few minutes, the strips can be put up on the board and discussed. Draw this shared activity together with previous learning by reminding the children about the key features of an adventure story using the display photocopiable sheet (page 11).

OBJECTIVES
■ To use a map as a way of planning an adventure story.
■ To identify moments of tension and excitement.

ADVENTURE MAPS
WHAT YOU NEED
Map outline (see below), paper, writing and drawing materials.

WHAT TO DO
Before you start this activity, sketch a rough map outline of an adventure setting on a large sheet of paper. Label a few significant features, such as a deep gorge with a fast-flowing river, a ruined temple, underground caves and so on. Display this and explain to the children how maps can be used to plan an adventure story. (Sometimes, a story like *The Secret World of Polly Flint* will include a map.) Start to build in more detail on the map using ideas from the children. As you are doing this, talk about what might happen to your characters in this landscape. Comments like *Someone could hide behind here*; *I wonder if they find treasure or danger here?*; *They could cross on a rope ladder* or *How could someone escape?* will help.

To extend and develop this work, let the children create their own adventure map in pairs. When they have completed this, they can be asked to make a note of some possible story events. This will draw on the comments you made in the shared activity (for example, the rope ladder breaks).

SEEING STARS

WHAT YOU NEED

Photocopiable page 16, writing and drawing materials.

WHAT TO DO

This activity helps children to develop some adventure characters, to think of their attributes and the particular quest they are on.

First explain to the children what a quest is. You could relate this to Polly Flint trying to find out who the Catcher is, or Lila's journey to find the Royal Sulphur. Then model a character plan of your own, based on photocopiable page 16. The heroine could be Erica Strong, for example, on a quest to find the treasures of Tutankhamun. She could be an expert in desert survival and reading hieroglyphs, but her weakness might be a fear of heights… and so on. Talk about how her strengths could feature in an adventure story, and how any flaws she has could be used to add interest and tension and help the reader identify with her as a 'real' person. Follow the same kind of process for a villain. The children can now work independently on the photocopiable sheet, designing characters of their own.

OBJECTIVES

■ To develop adventure characters (good and bad).

■ To explore possible tasks for the hero or heroine.

ON LOCATION

WHAT YOU NEED

Photocopiable page 17, writing materials.

WHAT TO DO

This activity helps children to think about the settings they can use in adventure story writing, and how these settings can intensify the action and challenge their characters. The activity can be used in conjunction with 'Adventure maps' on page 12 or as a follow-up to viewing a video extract.

Demonstrate how to select potential dangers (shown on the left-hand side of photocopiable page 17) to complete location notes. For example, you might underline *deep ravine* and *winding road* and then make notes: *chase scene – a bend in the road – road is wet – jeep swerves to avoid rock fall – Hannah is thrown out of jeep – will she be caught?* The children can work like this in pairs, choosing two or three of the danger words to use and make notes from. If appropriate, they could then go on to create other possible scenarios for discussion in a plenary session.

OBJECTIVES

■ To develop adventure story settings.

■ To think about how settings can influence a plot.

PULL THE TRIGGER

WHAT YOU NEED

Paper or whiteboards, writing materials, board or flip chart.

WHAT TO DO

Before you start this shared activity, draw four large boxes on the board, labelled *Event*, *Message*, *Object* and *Visitor*. Begin by reminding the children about the characteristics of adventure stories and use their appreciation of the points on photocopiable page 11 to gauge their growing understanding of the genre. Focus on the children's understanding of a 'trigger' event (you might liken it to a starting pistol for a race). Remind them how an adventure story often involves the main character in a journey or quest, and that the trigger is the starting or turning point: the intrigue that sets the main or further exciting events in motion.

Explain how you are going to experiment with different kinds of triggers. Remind the children about the extract from *The Secret World of Polly Flint* and make notes

OBJECTIVES

■ To think about events that get an adventure story started.

■ To consider how a trigger event can capture the reader's interest.

in the *Event* box based on this passage. (For example, *Polly sees ghost-like figure of a man with a net... who is he...? what is he doing...?*) Talk about different kinds of messages that are triggers and the various ways they can be received, such as phone calls, e-mails and postcards. Ask the children to work in pairs to jot down ideas for a trigger message. After a few minutes, you can discuss their ideas and choose one to write in the message box. Repeat the exercise for the *Objects* box (for example, a parcel, scroll, or map). In the *Visitors* box you might have *old friend, a strange tall man with a bad cough* and so on.

Conclude this session by talking about how the writer knows the full story, but keeps the reader guessing, and 'hooked', by revealing only little bits of information at a time. For example, the hero will eventually find the other half of a map that, after a perilous journey, leads to hidden treasure, *but* the trigger is having only half a map! The reader doesn't know how the hero will find the other half or where the map leads.

AN ELEMENT OF SURPRISE
WHAT YOU NEED
Photocopiable page 18, writing materials, paper.

WHAT TO DO
This will help children to think about specific events in their adventure stories which, by involving changes of mood and pace, surprise and grip the reader. It works well as a guided writing activity. Begin by getting the children to talk about occasions when they have been surprised or frightened. You might use an event from your own experience to get the discussion going. Talk about how you felt before and after the incident.

Now look at photocopiable page 18, using one of the suggestions from the discussion as the surprise. Encourage the children to think about giving a false sense of security – how an adventure hero may be resting, sleeping or walking without a care and all of a sudden something happens to change the mood. Talk about the atmosphere before and after (what the hero can hear, see and feel). Ask the children to jot their ideas on the photocopiable sheet, then discuss these as a group and talk about ways of increasing the element of surprise. Encourage the children to work on their own to write their surprise scene in continuous prose.

MEANWHILE...
WHAT YOU NEED
Photocopiable page 19, writing and drawing materials.

WHAT TO DO
This activity helps the children to develop tension in their adventure stories by recounting events that are happening at the same time.

Introduce the children to a possible adventure scenario in which tension is high – for example the hero could be imprisoned, trapped or tied up, whilst the enemy is near to completing the quest. This could then be represented as two freeze-frames in a role-play activity. Remind the children to think about the nature of the quest and the hero's predicament as they imagine the scenes. Now ask them to complete photocopiable page 19, sketching scenes on the left and making notes on the right. Draw the children's attention to the connecting words and phrases that emphasise two events occurring simultaneously.

OBJECTIVES
■ To plan events that surprise the reader.
■ To create sudden changes in mood and pace.

OBJECTIVES
■ To explore working with parallel events in adventure stories.
■ To experiment with the use of connective words and phrases.

SHOULD I STAY OR SHOULD I GO?

WHAT YOU NEED

Photocopiable page 20, writing materials, scissors, glue, paper.

WHAT TO DO

Organise a small group discussion to focus on 'decision points' in adventure stories. Explain how characters may be faced with a dilemma or difficult choice. Think about the effect that this can have on a reader. At a decision point, the reader is *anticipating* what may happen next and *identifying* with the character. Discuss the example on the photocopiable sheet, then talk about some of the other dilemmas. The children can work independently, cutting and pasting each of the scenarios and using the example as a model for recording possible consequences. As an extension activity, encourage the children to write a short excerpt based on one of the dilemmas.

OBJECTIVES

■ To explore points at which the main character is faced with a dilemma.

■ To look at critical moments in an adventure story.

CLIFFHANGERS

WHAT YOU NEED

Photocopiable page 21, writing materials.

WHAT TO DO

Establish the children's understanding of what a cliffhanger is and discuss how writers use this device to increase excitement and drama. Using the extract on photocopiable page 5, explain how Philip Pullman leaves his heroine in a tricky situation. Emphasise that he knows how things will work out, but the reader doesn't! Read through the three examples on photocopiable page 21 and choose one to use in shared writing of a couple of short paragraphs. Demonstrate how to use language and sentence construction to build up tension and to make the writing flow. To continue this scaffolding, ask the children to note two new examples that they can use in their adventure stories, encouraging them to expand one set of notes into a prose scene.

OBJECTIVES

■ To develop suspense in adventure story writing.

■ To generate situations in which the hero or heroine is in danger.

ROAD RAGE

WHAT YOU NEED

Enlarged copies of photocopiable page 22 (enough for one per pair), small toy vehicles or counters, dice, paper, writing materials.

WHAT TO DO

Introduce this activity by talking about chase scenes in films the children have seen. You may decide to watch a video extract in preparation. Explain how chase scenes introduce pace and excitement through fast action and changing fortunes. Explain how to play the game in pairs, using the dice to move along the board. If a player hits a shaded area, they are 'off the road', and must throw the dice again to identify a 'setback' to face. As they wait their next turn, they must note down a way of avoiding the setback and getting back on the road. They read this out when it is their turn in order to get back on the road. At the end of the game, collect the scraps of paper. These can now be used in shared writing to compose a chase extract from an adventure story. Emphasise how pace and excitement are conveyed in writing through changes in sentence length, through the use of connecting clauses (such as *all of a sudden; with a resounding crash*) and careful choice of verbs (for example, *smashed, swerved, stumbled* or *somersaulted*).

OBJECTIVES

■ To experiment with the idea of pace in adventure story writing.

■ To look at ways of building excitement through a chase scene.

writing guides: **ADVENTURE STORIES**

Seeing stars

Adventure stories need star characters. They need good characters
(heroes and heroines) and bad characters (villains).
Heroes have a task to achieve – villains get in the way!

Hero

Name _____

Quest _____

_____

Strengths _____

_____

Weakness(es) _____

_____

Mugshot

Villain

Name _____

Strengths _____

_____

_____

Weakness(es) _____

_____

_____

Mugshot

Now give a short history of these characters.

On location

Setting is important for an adventure story. You will need a dramatic landscape with lots of natural dangers, and buildings that are full of surprises, secrets and mysteries. Underline two or three features from each list and make notes on how you could use them in your story.

tropical rainforest

sandy desert

deep ravine

volcano

cliff face

fast-flowing river

quicksand

winding road

avalanche

Landscape location

secret doorway

underground passage

trapdoor

wall paintings

remote castle

crumbling pillars

abandoned temple

ancient tomb

Building location

An element of surprise

Think about how you will surprise your reader, for example a door bursts open, your hero falls through a trapdoor, or the villain attacks. What happens before and after the surprise event?

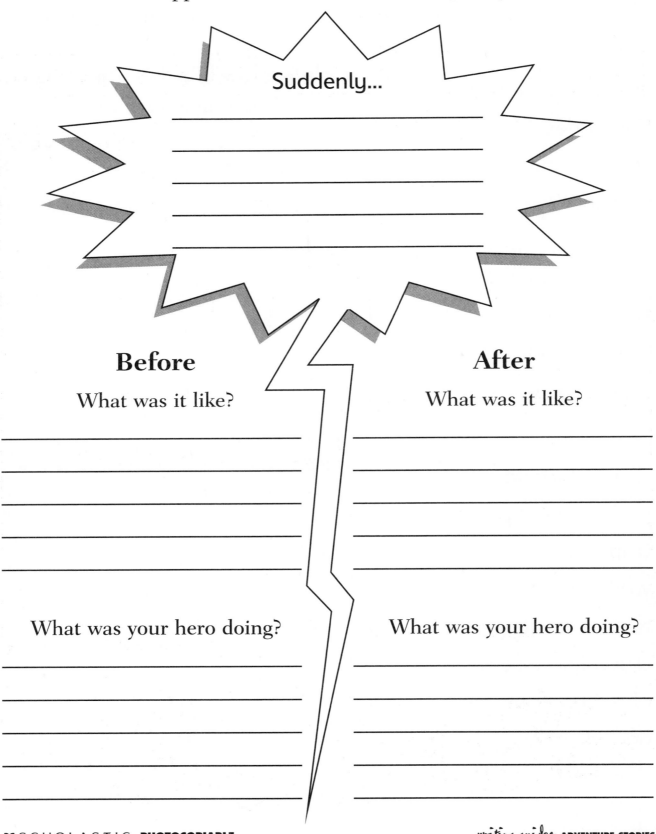

Suddenly...

_____

_____

_____

_____

_____

Before

What was it like?

_____

_____

_____

_____

What was your hero doing?

_____

_____

_____

After

What was it like?

_____

_____

_____

_____

What was your hero doing?

_____

_____

_____

Meanwhile...

Sometimes two things will be happening at the same time in your adventure story. Perhaps your heroine is trapped just as the villain is about to find the treasure. Sketch two events in the boxes and describe what is going on. Join the two events with words like:

at the same time	meanwhile	while this was going on

Event 1

Event 2

Writer's notebook

Should I stay or should I go?

Sometimes your hero or heroine will be faced with a difficult choice – a choice where there is possible DANGER! Cut out the four pictures below and think of good and bad consequences like those in the example.

writing guides: ADVENTURE STORIES

Cliffhangers

Place your hero or heroine in a tricky situation. How much
you tell the reader about the situation and how much you don't
will help to make your adventure story exciting. Read these examples,
then think of two tricky situations of your own.
Choose one of them to write as a passage.

What will you tell the reader?	What won't you tell the reader?
Your heroine is trapped in a dark, damp cellar.	Her friend will rescue her through a secret tunnel.

Road rage

Imagine you are a character in an adventure story and you are being chased. Choose your vehicle! Throw the dice. If you land on a shaded square, throw the dice again to select the setback. Miss a turn while you jot down what you could do about it. Read your solution out to get back on the road when it's your turn.

1

Flat tyre. You skid off the road!

2

Rock fall. Your vehicle crashes!

3

Fireball. You brake suddenly!

4

Ice on the road. You hit a tree!

5

Wounded in the arm. You lose control!

6

Out of fuel. You grind to a halt!

Finish

Start

writing guides: **ADVENTURE STORIES**

This section helps the children to develop their writing from the ideas planned in Section Two. The activities are designed so that the children focus on one aspect of their adventure story writing each time. They deal with building tension through entrapment and escape, creating a dangerous quest scenario, and developing the overall shape of the adventure. Before starting this section, it will be useful for the children to finalise their story plans. This is important whether they are working individually or collaboratively. The activities in Section Two will have generated plenty of material for this. Encourage the children to use a large sheet of paper as a story plan reminder. They can jot notes, make sketches or attach worksheets from the first two sections to this planner.

In the beginning...

The children can use this sheet to write the beginning of their adventure stories. Encourage them to use their knowledge of the genre from their own reading or viewing, as well as what they have learned of readers' expectations from working through this guide. The questions in speech bubbles are prompts that identify information that the reader needs to know in order to make sense of and develop interest in the story. The first box introduces the hero or heroine. Ask the children to think about where their heroine is. Perhaps she is relaxing, going about her daily life when the adventure begins. Remind the children that they can reveal something of a character's feelings and personality through what she does and says. Remind the children of their work on trigger events (page 13 and photocopiable page 18) for the second box. For the background, the children need to think about what sort of information about the quest they want to introduce at this point. The activity concludes by asking children to identify the first stages of a journey. Encourage the children to complete the boxes in full sentences, drafting their story openings.

Dangerous quest

To complete this sheet, the children will be writing a scene in which their hero or heroine encounters a dangerous situation (which is set inside the archway) and finds something that is crucial in the quest (represented by 'Found'). This is important for developing the middle part of the children's stories. The hero then has to make a quick getaway that involves a chase. Remind the children of their work on chases from photocopiable page 22. This activity involves several changes in mood and pace. Children can plan their presentation of this incident independently and then use this sheet to work on their drafts in a guided writing session.

Spirit of adventure

To help build excitement and anticipation into their stories, the children can use this sheet to write about a moment of tension in which their adventure hero or heroine is trapped. They will need to work hard to build excitement into this piece of writing. It needs to give the reader a false sense of security (see, for example, 'An element of surprise' on page 14) and be dramatic! Explain to the children that you want them to indicate the hero's changing fortunes. So, for example, after being trapped, he escapes – there is a sense of exhilaration that quickly turns to fear as he faces a fresh danger. Encourage them to write as vividly as they can, so the reader is 'with' the hero as he or she reads.

In the beginning...

Use this framework to work on the beginning of your story. Look at the reader's questions to help you.

The hero

Where is your hero?

What is your hero doing?

The trigger

What happens?

What's the mystery?

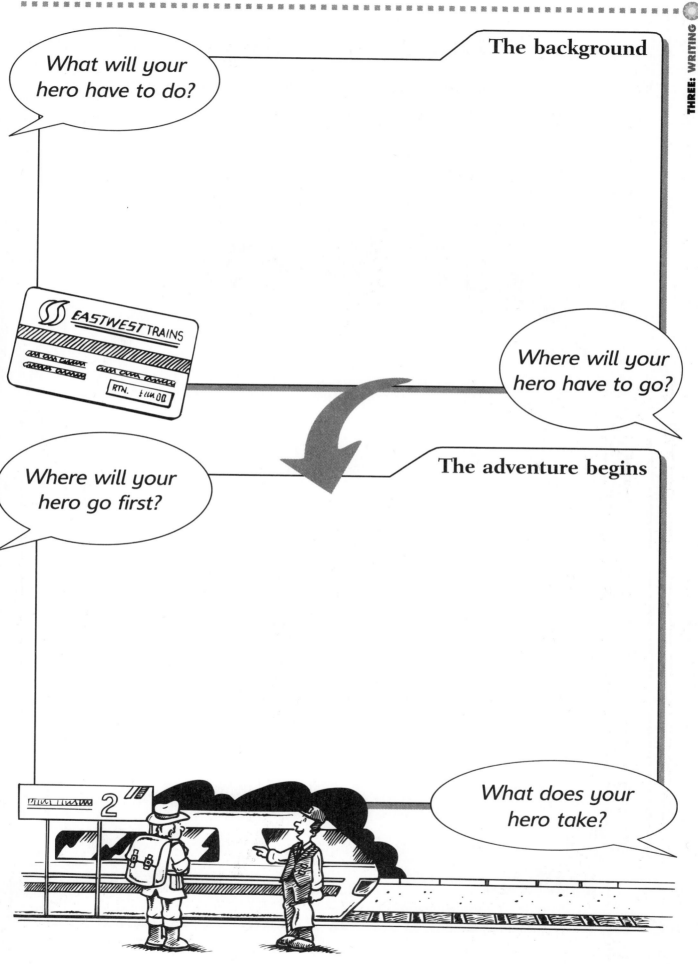

The background

What will your hero have to do?

Where will your hero have to go?

The adventure begins

Where will your hero go first?

What does your hero take?

EASTWEST TRAINS

RTN.

Dangerous quest

Work on an exciting episode in your story. There is danger, the hero completes part of the quest, and then there is a chase…

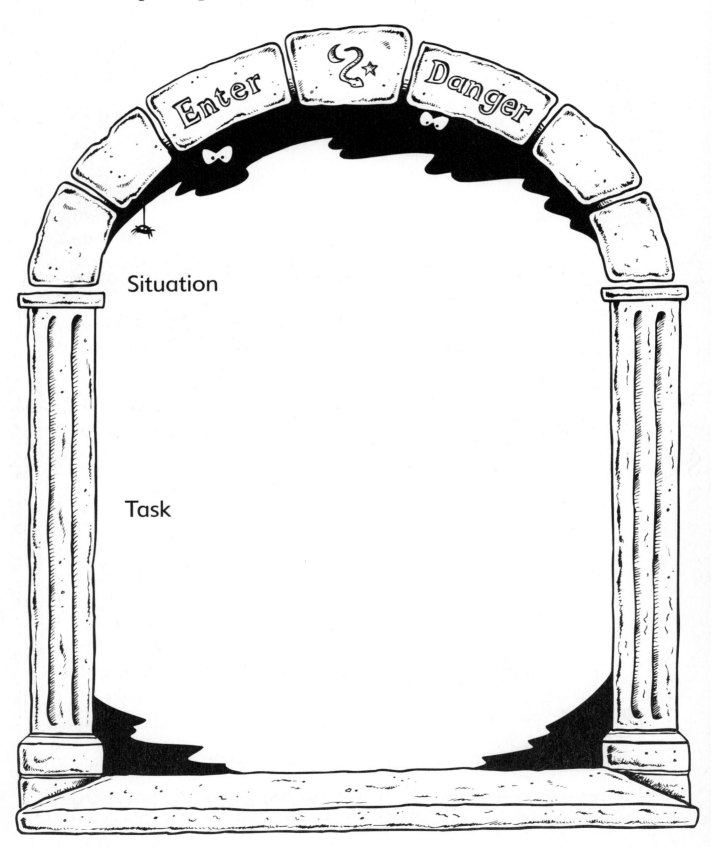

Situation

Task

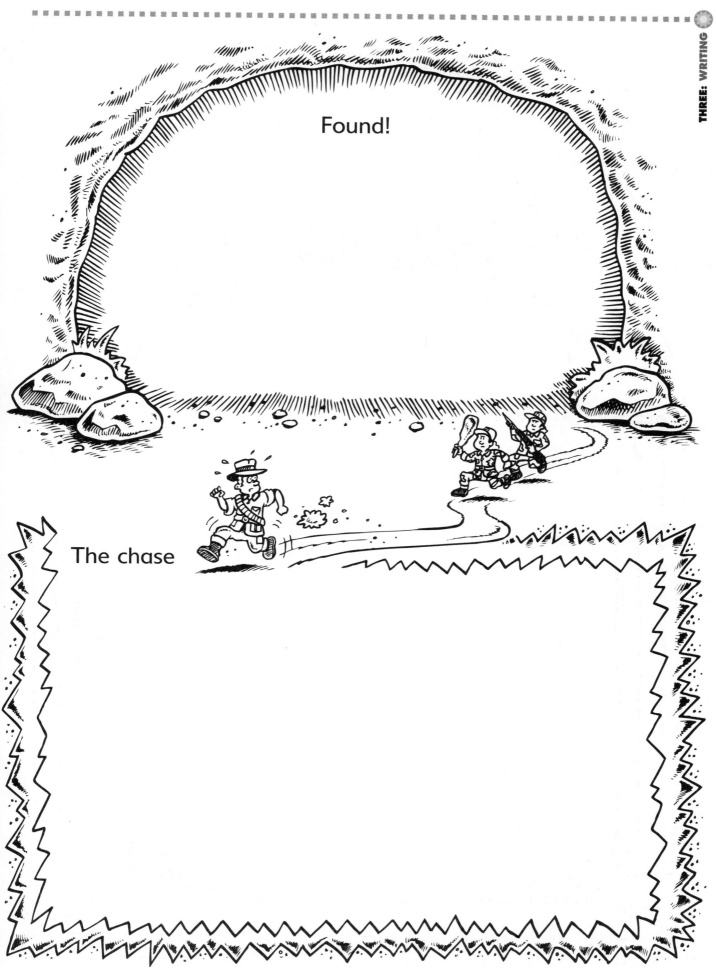

Found!

The chase

Spirit of adventure

Use these prompts to work on a part of your story that is full of suspense and shows your hero's spirit and strong temperament. What does he go through and how does he face these tests? Describe the changing pace and mood.

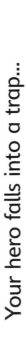

Your hero falls into a trap...

Make this a surprise!

Introduce fear!

and meets more danger!

Make this fast!

escapes...

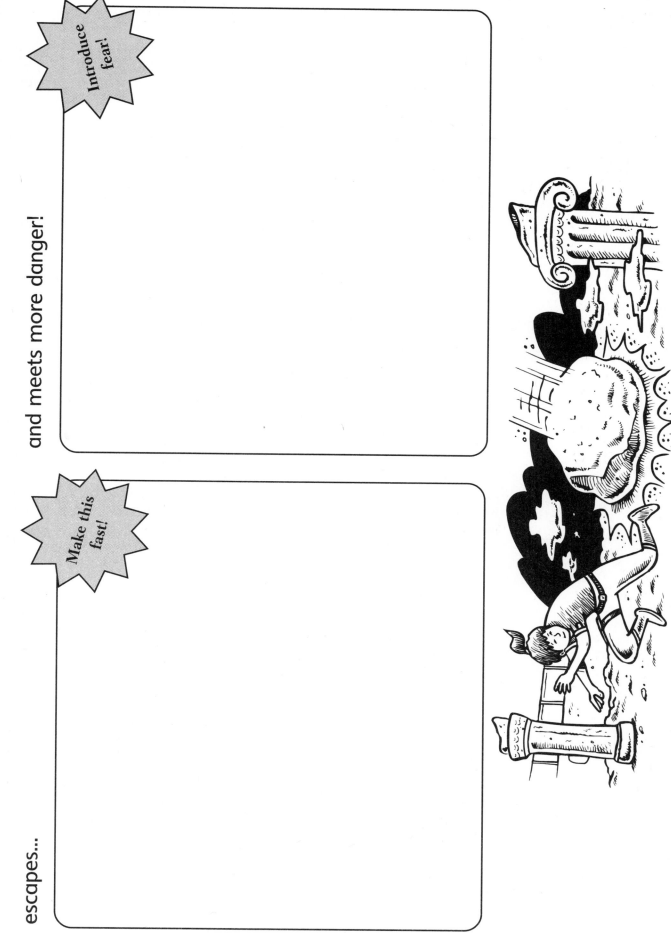

SECTION FOUR
REVIEW

This section provides guidance on helping children to identify what they have learned about adventure story writing and to look at the strengths and weaknesses of the work that they have produced. Two photocopiable activities guide this process of reflection.

In your own assessment of children's work it will be important to evaluate their progress against a variety of objectives. In doing this, you may want to look at what they have produced at various stages in the writing project as well as the final story itself. For instance, their work from activities in Section Two may well present good evidence of their achievement in generating ideas or developing descriptive techniques. If they have a writer's notebook, this will be useful in assessing their understanding of the writing process.

Try to make good use of writing audiences. You may be able to use a parallel class in your own school or form a writing partnership with another school. Many of the activities the children have worked on ask them to think about how, as writers, they will entertain, excite or surprise the reader. Readers' feedback, such as that stimulated by photocopiable page 31, will be very helpful. You can use this to help children to set personal writing targets. These can refer to adventure story writing or broader writing activities.

How was it for you?
This activity encourages children to evaluate the adventure stories that they have written and the particular writing techniques that they have developed. The activity considers characterisation, and the description of excitement and danger. It concludes with a consideration of how the story could be improved. Advise the children that they, as writers, need to write in the right-hand column of photocopiable page 31. They can then ask a friend or writing partner to give his or her feedback in the left-hand column. The sheet can be folded in half to encourage an original response, not influenced by the writer's comments. It is often useful to talk to children about ways of responding to each other's writing – making sure that they include positive points whilst still being critical. Encourage both the writer and reader to give reasons for their answers to the questions on the sheet.

What an adventure story!
Before you start this activity, ask the children to reflect on what they have learned about adventure story writing through working on this project. Tell them to think about the key features of an adventure story introduced in Section One, identifying how they have used these in their writing. Have a brief discussion, before asking the children to complete photocopiable page 32 individually.

writing guides: **ADVENTURE STORIES**

How was it for you?

Review your adventure story. Read the questions and write your answers under **The writer** heading. Ask a friend who has read your story to write his or her comments under **The reader** heading.

The reader	The writer
Who were your favourite characters?	Who were your favourite characters?
What was the most exciting part?	What was the most exciting part?
What was the most dangerous part?	What was the most dangerous part?
What would make the adventure better?	What would make the adventure better?

What an adventure story!

Make a note of how you included the following features in your adventure story.

Missions or quests

Dramatic settings

Dangerous situations

Changes of pace

Chase and escape

Cliffhangers

Surprises

writing guides: **ADVENTURE STORIES**